ISBN 0-7918-2319-9

9 780791 823194

N08096

S0-EAQ-817

The American Society of Mechanical Engineers

AN AMERICAN NATIONAL STANDARD

SURFACE TEXTURE SYMBOLS

ASME Y14.36M-1996

[Revision of ANSI Y14.36-1978 (R1993)]

Date of Issuance: August 13, 1996

This Standard will be revised when the Society approves the issuance of a new edition. There will be no addenda or written interpretations of the requirements of this Standard issued to this edition.

ASME is the registered trademark of The American Society of Mechanical Engineers.

This code or standard was developed under procedures accredited as meeting the criteria for American National Standards. The Consensus Committee that approved the code or standard was balanced to assure that individuals from competent and concerned interests have had an opportunity to participate. The proposed code or standard was made available for public review and comment which provides an opportunity for additional public input from industry, academia, regulatory agencies, and the public-at-large.

ASME does not "approve," "rate," or "endorse" any item, construction, proprietary device, or activity.

ASME does not take any position with respect to the validity of any patent rights asserted in connection with any items mentioned in this document, and does not undertake to insure anyone utilizing a standard against liability for infringement of any applicable Letters Patent, nor assume any such liability. Users of a code or standard are expressly advised that the determination of the validity of any such patent rights, and the risk of the infringement of such rights, is entirely their own responsibility.

Participation by federal agency representative(s) or persons(s) affiliated with industry is not to be interpreted as government or industry endorsement of this code or standard.

ASME accepts responsibility for only those interpretations issued in accordance with governing ASME procedures and policies which preclude the issuance of interpretations by individual volunteers.

No part of this document may be reproduced in any form,
in an electronic retrieval system or otherwise,
without the prior written permission of the publisher.

The American Society of Mechanical Engineers
345 E. 47th Street   New York, NY   10017

Copyright © 1996 by
THE AMERICAN SOCIETY OF MECHANICAL ENGINEERS
All Rights Reserved
Printed in U.S.A.

FOREWORD

(This Foreword is not part of ASME Y14.36M-1996.)

Subcommittee 36, Surface Texture Symbols, was formed in November 1974, and is a Subcommittee of the ASME Standards Committee Y14, Engineering Drawing and Related Documentation Practices. The Subcommittee is charged with the responsibility of establishing surface texture symbols, and methods for specifying them on engineering drawings.

The basis for this Standard is ASME B46.1-1995, Surface Texture, which covers other subjects related to surface texture, such as definitions of terms, instrumentation, precision reference specimens, roughness comparison specimens, and reference material such as notes on use and interpretation of profiling instruments, control and production of surface texture, and other methods of specification and measurement of surface qualities.

This revision is also based on a review of and conforms in most respects with the international standard ISO 1302:1992, Technical Drawings—Method of Indicating Surface Texture.

The following is a summary of the significant changes made to the 1978 Edition of this Standard.

(a) The waviness designation is invoked by W_t and a value placed in the symbol;

(b) roughness values other than R_a now have a place in the symbol;

(c) other parameters can be invoked by a note;

(d) the location in the symbol for designating processes now conforms with ISO 1302:1992;

(e) the roughness cutoff or sampling length no longer has a default value of 0.8 mm (.030 in.).

Suggestions for improvement of this Standard will be welcome. They should be sent to The American Society of Mechanical Engineers, Att: Secretary, Y14 Main Committee, 345 East 47th Street, New York, NY 10017.

This revision was approved as an American National Standard on February 5, 1996

ASME STANDARDS COMMITTEE Y14
Engineering Drawing and Related Documentation Practices

(The following is the roster of the Committee at the time of approval of this Standard.)

OFFICERS

F. Bakos, Jr., *Chair*
A. R. Anderson, *Vice Chair*
C. J. Gomez, *Secretary*

COMMITTEE PERSONNEL

A. R. Anderson, Dimensional Control Systems
F. Bakos, Jr., Eastman Kodak Co.
D. E. Bowerman, Copeland Corporation
J. V. Burleigh, The Boeing Company
R. A. Chadderdon, Southwest Consultants
F. A. Christiana, ASEA Brown Boveri Combustion Engineering Systems
M. E. Curtis, Rexnord Corporation
R. W. DeBolt, Motorola, Government and Space Technology Group
H. L Dubocq
L. W. Foster, L. W. Foster Associates, Inc.
D. Hagler, E-Systems Inc., Garland Division
C. G. Lance, Santa Cruz Technology Center
P. E. McKim, Caterpillar Inc.
C. D. Merkley, IBM Corporation
E. Niemiec, Westinghouse Electric Corporation
R. J. Polizzi
D. L Ragon, Deere & Company, John Deere Dubuque Works
R. L Tennis, Caterpillar Inc.
R. P. Tremblay, U.S. Department of the Army, ARDEC
R. K. Walker, Westinghouse Marine
G. H. Whitmire, TEC/TREND
K. Wiegandt, Sandia National Laboratory
P. Wreede, E-Systems, Inc.

SUBCOMMITTEE 36 — SURFACE TEXTURE SYMBOLS

M. E. Curtis, *Chair*, Rexnord Corporation
T. D. Benoit, Pratt & Whitney
E. E. Brockway, Caterpillar Inc.
J. G. Liska, Aerojet, Propulsion Division
P. J. McQuistion, Ohio University
J. D. Meadows, Institute for Engineering and Design Inc.
R.P. Tremblay, U.S. Department of the Army, ARD

CONTENTS

Foreword iii
Standards Committee Roster v

1 General 1
   1.1 Scope 1
   1.2 Units 1
   1.3 Application 1
   1.4 Definitions and Description of Measurement Methods 1

2 Applicable Documents 1

3 Surface Texture Symbol 1
   3.1 Symbol 1
   3.2 Control 3

4 Application of Symbols and Values 3
   4.1 Value Application 3
   4.2 Measurements 3
   4.3 Roughness Average (R_a) 3
   4.4 Roughness Cutoff or Sampling Length 3
   4.5 Roughness Parameters Other Than R_a 3
   4.6 Waviness Height 4
   4.7 Lay 4
   4.8 Designations Other Than ASME B46.1-1995 Defaults 4

5 Example Designations 4
   5.1 Examples 4
   5.2 Symbols for Special or Multiple Operations 4

Figures
1 Surface Texture Symbols and Construction 2
2 Location of Surface Texture Symbols 3
3 Symbol Value Application 3
4 Lay Symbols 5
5 Examples of Surface Texture Symbol Application 6
6 Examples of Special Designations 7

ENGINEERING DRAWING AND RELATED DOCUMENTATION PRACTICES

SURFACE TEXTURE SYMBOLS

1 GENERAL

1.1 Scope

This Standard establishes the method to designate controls for surface texture of solid materials. It includes methods for controlling roughness, waviness, and lay by providing a set of symbols for use on drawings, specifications, or other documents (see Fig. 1).

This Standard does not specify the means by which the surface texture is to be produced or measured.

1.2 Units

The units shall be consistent with the other units used on the drawing or document. The numeric values expressed in this Standard are stated in SI metric and are to be regarded as standard. It should be understood that U.S. customary units could equally have been used without prejudice to the principles established. Approximate nonmetric equivalents are shown for reference in ASME B46.1.

1.3 Application

When required from a functional standpoint, the desired surface characteristics shall be specified. Where no surface texture control is specified, the surface produced is satisfactory provided it is within the limits of size (and form) specified in accordance with ASME Y14.5M. Surface texture values, unless otherwise specified, apply to the finished surface. Preferably, there should always be some maximum value of the desired surface characteristic, either noted specifically or by default (for example, in the manner of the "UNLESS OTHERWISE SPECIFIED" note shown in Fig. 2).

1.4 Definitions and Description of Measurement Methods

This Standard does not provide surface texture definitions or measurement methods. These subjects are defined in ASME B46.1.

2 APPLICABLE DOCUMENTS

When the following American National Standards referred to in this Standard are superseded by a revision approved by the American National Standards Institute, Inc., the revision shall apply. The listed standards apply to the extent referenced herein.

ASME B46.1-1995, Surface Texture (Surface Roughness, Waviness and Lay)
ASME Y14.2M - 1992, Line Conventions and Lettering
ASME Y14.5M - 1994, Dimensioning and Tolerancing

3 SURFACE TEXTURE SYMBOL

3.1 Symbol

The symbol used to designate control of surface texture is shown in Fig. 1(a). Where surface texture symbols are used with values, the symbol must be drawn with the horizontal extension as show in Fig. 1(e). Symbols used without values must have their meaning explained in a note on the drawing (see Fig. 2).

3.1.1 Material Removal Required or Prohibited. The surface texture symbol is modified when necessary to require or prohibit removal of material. When it is necessary to indicate that a surface must be produced by removal of material by machining, specify the symbol shown in Fig. 1(b). When required, the minimum amount of material to be removed is specified as shown in Fig. 1(c). When it is necessary to indicate that a surface must be produced without material removal, specify the machining prohibited symbol as shown in Fig. 1(d). If the symbols are used without values they must have their meaning explained in a note on the drawing (see Fig. 2).

3.1.2 Symbol Proportions. The recommended proportions for drawing the surface texture symbol are shown in Fig. 1(f). The letter height and line width should be the same as that prescribed for dimensions and dimension lines. See ASME Y14.2M.

3.1.3 Symbol Location. The point of the symbol shall be on a line representing the surface, an extension line of the surface, or a leader line directed to the surface, or to an extension line. The symbol may be specified following a diameter dimension. The long leg (and extension) shall be to the right as the drawing is read (reading direction practices are set forth in ASME Y14.5M, and line practices are in ASME Y14.2M.) A

ASME Y14.36M-1996   SURFACE TEXTURE SYMBOLS

	Symbol	Meaning
(a) 	∨	Basic Surface Texture Symbol. Surface may be produced by any method except when the bar or circle (Symbol b or d) is specified.
(b) 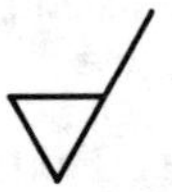	∀	Material Removal By Machining Is Required. The horizontal bar indicates material removal by machining is required to produce the surface and material must be provided for that purpose.
(c) 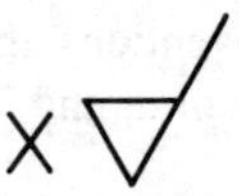	X ∀	Material Removal Allowance. Value in millimeters for "X" defines the minimum material removal requirement.
(d) 	∨ with circle	Material Removal Prohibited. The circle in the vee indicates the surface must be produced by processes such as casting, forging, hot finishing, cold finishing, die casting, powder metallurgy or injection molding without subsequent removal of material.
(e) 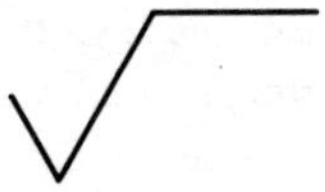	∨	Surface Texture Symbol. To be used when any surface texture values, production method, treatment, coating or other text are specified above the horizontal line or to the right of the symbol. Surface may be produced by any method except when bar or circle (Symbol b or d) is specified or when the method is specified above the horizontal line.

(f) Construction dimensions:
- 3X minimum *
- 1.5X
- 3X approx
- 3X
- 60°, 60°
- 1.5X
- letter height = X

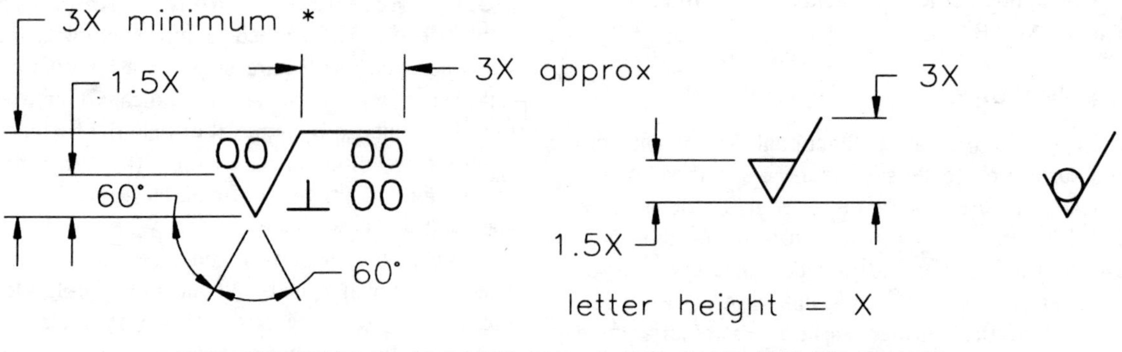

* THIS DIMENSION IS ADJUSTED BY +1 FOR EACH LINE OF VALUES BEYOND THE TWO LINES SHOWN BELOW THE HORIZONTAL LINE.

FIG. 1 SURFACE TEXTURE SYMBOLS AND CONSTRUCTION

surface texture symbol may be used without values. In this case, a general note must be added to the drawing which applies to each surface texture symbol specified without values. See Fig. 2.

3.2 Control

When the symbol is used, it affects the entire surface defined by dimensioning. Areas of transition, such as chamfers and fillets, shall conform with the roughest adjacent finished area unless otherwise indicated.

3.2.1 Plated or Coated Surfaces.
Drawings or specifications for plated or coated parts shall indicate whether the surface texture values apply before, after, or both before and after plating or coating.

4 APPLICATION OF SYMBOLS AND VALUES

4.1 Value Application

Include in the symbol only those values required to specify and verify the required surface texture characteristics. The units used shall be the same as that used for the drawing in general. The configuration of the symbol and applied relevant requirements shown shall be as shown in Fig. 3.

4.2 Measurements

Measurements, unless otherwise specified, shall apply in a direction which gives the maximum reading; generally across the lay.

4.3 Roughness Average (R_a)

The principal parameter specified for roughness is the roughness average, R_a, defined in ASME B46.1. Its value is shown in position "a" of the surface texture symbol in Fig. 3.

4.4 Roughness Cutoff or Sampling Length

Standard ratings are listed in Section 9 of ASME B46.1 with some selection criteria given in Section 3 of ASME B46.1. Drawings prepared six months after the date of issuance of ASME B46.1-1995 shall state the roughness cutoff or sampling length in position "c" of Fig. 3.

NOTE: Prior to the adoption of ASME B46.1-1995 the default rating was 0.8 mm if no other rating was stated.

4.5 Roughness Parameters Other Than R_a

Roughness parameters other than R_a are designated to the right [position (f) in Fig. 3] of the cutoff rating.

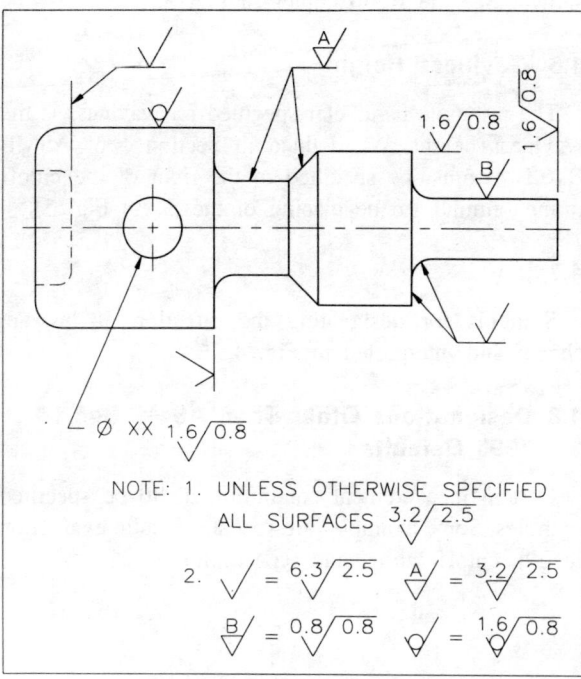

FIG. 2 LOCATION OF SURFACE TEXTURE SYMBOLS

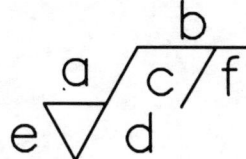

a = roughness value R_a in micrometers

b = production method, treatment, coating, other text, or note callout

c = roughness cutoff or sampling length in millimeters

d = direction of lay

e = minimum material removal requirement in millimeters

f = roughness value other than R_a in micrometers preceded by its parameter symbol (e.g. R_z 0.4)

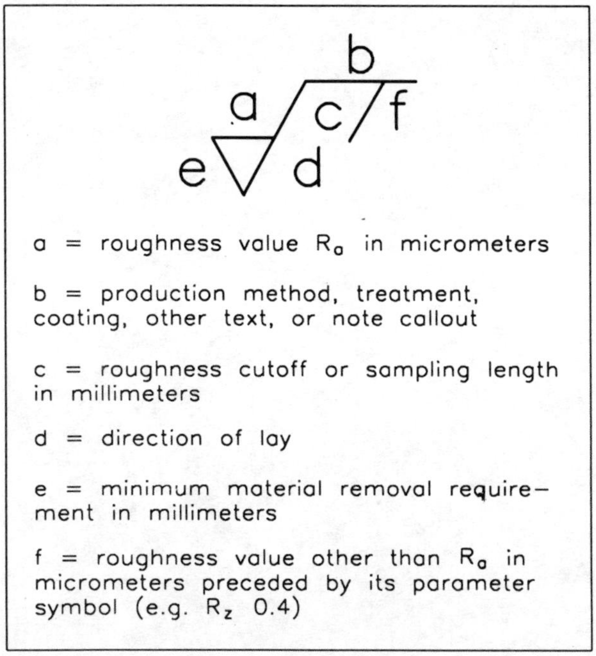

FIG. 3 SYMBOL VALUE APPLICATION

Both the symbol and the numerical value must be shown. See the R_z examples in Fig. 5.

4.6 Waviness Height

The principle parameter specified for waviness is the waviness height, W_t, defined in Section 1 of ASME B46.1. It must be specified to the right of the cutoff rating (similar to the placing of the S_m in Fig. 5).

4.7 Lay

Symbols for designating the direction of lay are shown and interpreted in Fig. 4.

4.8 Designations Other Than ASME B46.1-1995 Defaults

Certain measurement conditions are to be specified by notes. Some examples are special tip radii, evaluation length, cutoff rating, and type of filter.

5 EXAMPLE DESIGNATIONS

5.1 Examples

Fig. 5 illustrates examples of designations of R_a, lay, and roughness parameters other than R_a by insertion of values in appropriate positions relative to the symbol.

5.2 Symbols for Special or Multiple Operations

When surface roughness control of several operations is required within a given area, or on a given surface, surface qualities may be designated as in Fig. 6(a). If a surface must be produced by one particular process or a series of processes, they shall be specified as shown in Fig. 6(b). Where a surface requirement is needed on a portion of a designated surface, a note should be added at the symbol giving the requirements and the area involved. An example is illustrated in Fig. 6(c).

SURFACE TEXTURE SYMBOLS   ASME Y14.36M-1996

Lay Symbol	Meaning	Example Showing Direction of Tool Marks
=	Lay approximately parallel to the line representing the surface to which the symbol is applied.	
⊥	Lay approximately perpendicular to the line representing the surface to which the symbol is applied.	
X	Lay angular in both directions to the line representing the surface to which the symbol is applied.	
M	Lay multidirectional.	
C	Lay approximately circular relative to the center of the surface to which the symbol is applied.	
R	Lay approximately radial relative to the center of the surface to which the symbol is applied.	
P	Lay particulate, non-directional, or protuberant.	

FIG. 4 LAY SYMBOLS

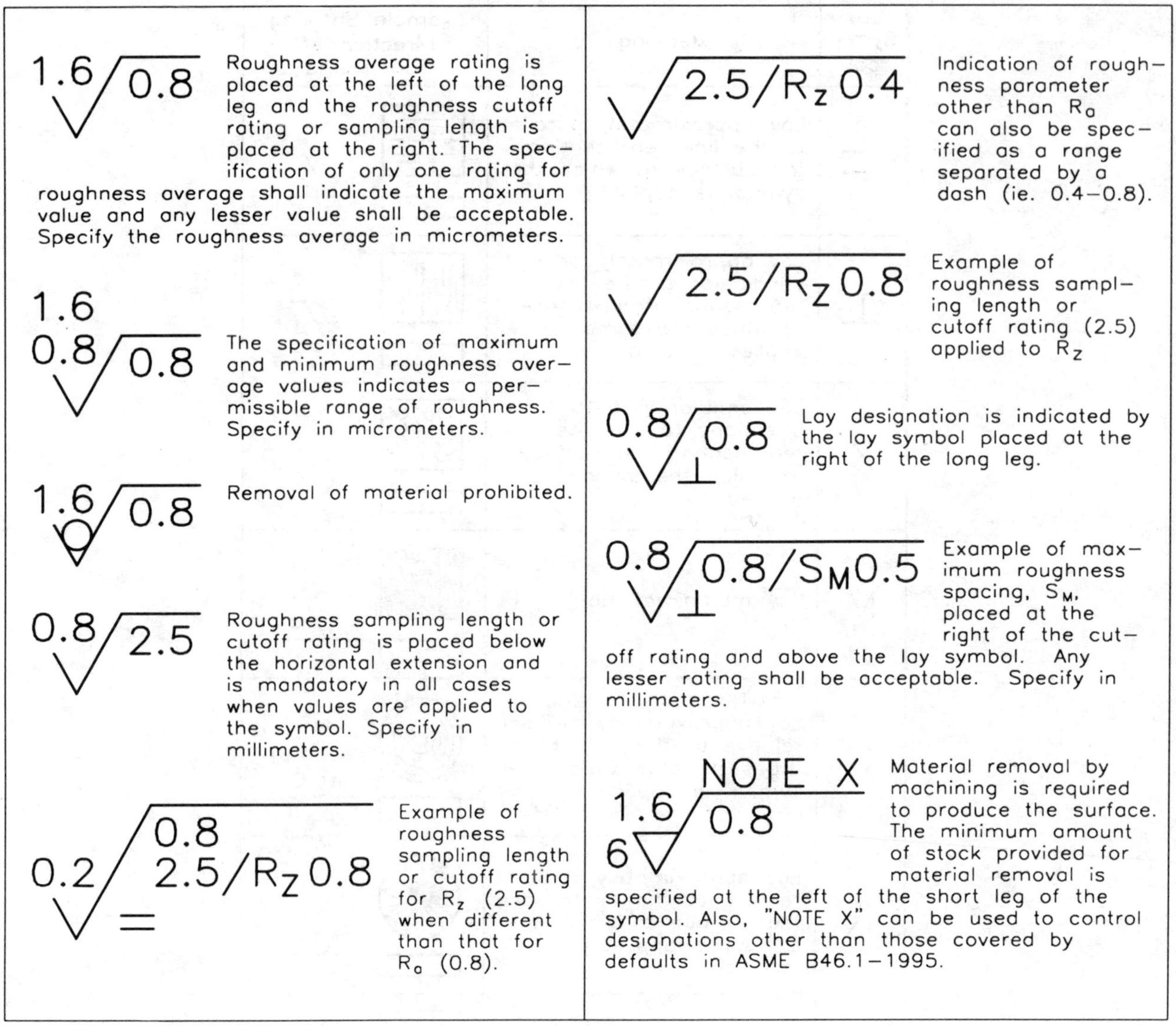

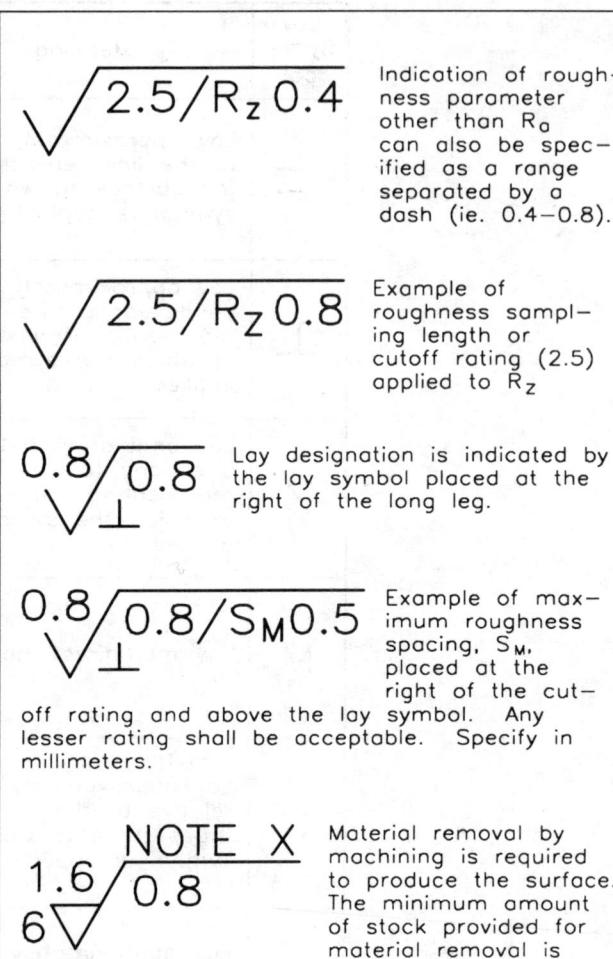

FIG. 5 EXAMPLES OF SURFACE TEXTURE SYMBOL APPLICATION

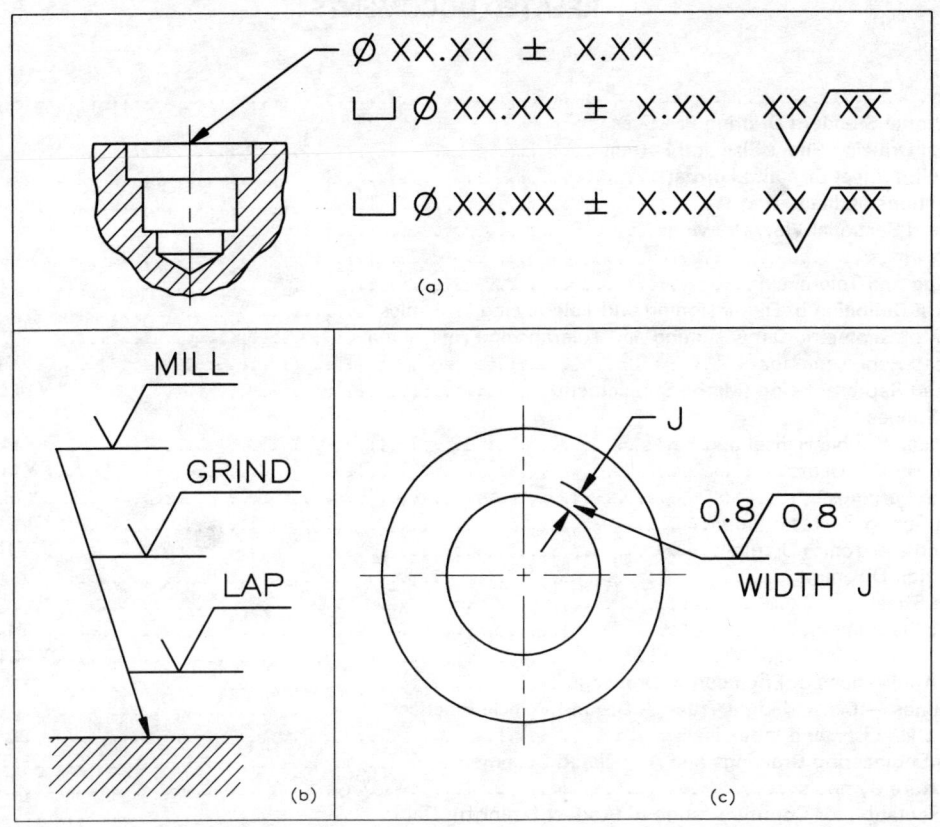

FIG. 6 EXAMPLES OF SPECIAL DESIGNATIONS

RELATED DOCUMENTS

Abbreviations Y1.1-1989
American National Standard Drafting Practices
    Decimal Inch Drawing Sheet Size and Format Y14.1-1995
    Metric Drawing Sheet Size and Format Y14.1M-1995
    Line Conventions and Lettering Y14.2M-1992
    Multiview and Sectional View Drawings Y14.3M-1994
    Pictorial Drawings .... Y14.4M-1989(R1994)
    Dimensioning and Tolerancing Y14.5M-1994
    Mathematical Definition of Dimensioning and Tolerancing Principles Y14.5.1M-1994
    Certification of Geometric Dimensioning and Tolerancing Professionals Y14.5.2M-1995
    Screw Thread Representation .... Y14.6-1978(R1993)
    Screw Thread Representation (Metric Supplement) .... Y14.6aM-1981(R1993)
    Gears and Splines
        Spur, Helical, Double Helical and Racks .... Y14.7.1-1971(R1993)
        Bevel and Hypoid Gears .... Y14.7.2-1978(R1994)
    Castings and Forgings .... Y14.8M-1989(R1993)
    Mechanical Spring Representation .... Y14.13M-1981(R1992)
    Electrical and Electronics Diagrams .... Y14.15-1966(R1988)
    Interconnection Diagrams Y14.15a-1971
    Information Sheet Y14.15b-1973
    Fluid Power Diagrams .... Y14.17-1966(R1987)
    Optical Parts .... Y14.18M-1986(R1993)
    Types and Applications of Engineering Drawings Y14.24M-1989
    Chassis Frames — Car and Light Truck — Ground Vehicle Practices Y14.32.1M-1994
    Parts Lists, Data Lists, and Index Lists Y14.34M-1989
    Revision of Engineering Drawings and Associated Documents Y14.35M-1992
    Surface Texture Symbols Y14.36M-1996
Digital Representation for Communication of Product Definition Data Y14.26M-1987
A Structural Language Format for Basic Shape Description .... Y14 Technical Report 4-1989
Illustrations for Publication and Projection .... Y15.1M-1979(R1986)
Time Series Charts .... Y15.2M-1979(R1986)
Process Charts .... Y15.3M-1979(R1986)
Graphic Symbols for:
    Electrical and Electronics Diagrams Y32.2-1975
    Plumbing .... Y32.4-1977(R1994)
    Railroad Maps and Profiles .... Y32.7-1972(R1994)
    Fluid Power Diagrams .... Y32.10-1967(R1994)
    Process Flow Diagrams in Petroleum and Chemical Industries .... Y32.11-1961(R1993)
    Mechanical and Acoustical Elements as Used in Schematic Diagrams .... Y32.18-1972(R1993)
    Pipe Fittings, Valves, and Piping .... Y32.2.3-1949(R1994)
    Heating, Ventilating, and Air Conditioning .... Y32.2.4-1949(R1993)
    Heat Power Apparatus .... Y32.2.6-1950(R1993)
Letter Symbols for:
    Glossary of Terms Concerning Letter Symbols .... Y10.1-1972(R1988)
    Mechanics and Time-Related Phenomena Y10.3M-1984
    Heat and Thermodynamics .... Y10.4-1982(R1988)
    Quantities Used in Electrical Science and Electrical Engineering Y10.5-1968
    Acoustics Y10.11-1984
    Chemical Engineering .... Y10.12-1955(R1988)
    Guide for Selecting Greek Letters Used as Letter Symbols for Engineering Mathematics ...... Y10.17-1961(R1988)
    Illuminating Engineering .... Y10.18-1967(R1987)

The ASME Publications Catalog shows a complete list of all the Standards published by the Society. For a complimentary catalog, or the latest information about our publications, call 1-800-THE-ASME (1-800-843-2763).